D1596808

Make Time To Heal

Qigong Practice Tips
for People with Parkinson's

BIANCA MOLLÉ, M.ED.

Edited by

Clare Henjum

METTAMORPHIX PRESS

Mettamorphix Press
www.mettamorphix.com
First Edition: April 2018

ISBN 978-0-9898072-1-0

The publisher is not responsible for websites (or their content) that are not owned by the publisher.

Cover, Book Design and Production by Clare Henjum
Production support by Isaiah Singer

*To all my friends and clients
who have enriched my practice, and
for allowing me to enrich theirs.*

About Bianca Mollé

 Author and coaching consultant, Bianca Mollé speaks internationally about the wellness strategies of Qigong that were key to her healing from Parkinson's Disease. She motivates others to discover these skills, sharing the tools of the mind-body practice of Wisdom Healing Qigong that can be beneficial to Parkinson's and many other chronic health conditions.

No stranger to challenge, she attributes her own discipline and innovation to being a parent of an autistic son and to being a credentialed teacher in both regular and special education for over 30 years. She now offers consulting support at Mettamorphix.com to help people discover and deepen their practice in Wisdom Healing Qigong. Bianca is the author of *Reboot and Rejoice: How I healed from Parkinson's Disease using the body-mind practice of Qigong.*

Contents

DISCLAIMER

Please consult with a medical professional
before starting any exercise program. The
information in this book is not intended
to provide medical advice or to replace
or change your medical care or treatment
program. Always consult with a medical
professional whenever you are considering
any changes to your medical program or
medications.

In Gratitude

A universe of gratitude and thanks goes to Dr. Pang Ming, who created the form of Qigong that healed me from Parkinson's Disease. Tremendous gratitude as well goes to Master Mingtong Gu, my main teacher and a student of Dr. Pang, who brought Wisdom Healing Qigong here to the U.S. from China. To Teachers Ma, Zhao, and Zheng, my angels at the China retreat, I thank you, and please know that distance and language are no barriers to the healing love graciously shared. It is returned with enthusiasm. To Linling Xie, many thanks for your many acts of kindness. To the entire world qigong community: Thank you for your continuing work by which we connect to each other with compassion and benevolence. The world is a better place because of you.

There is also a cadre of blessed beings who came along after my recovery and shared with me the journey forward. You helped me to understand my "new" self and to progress in what is my new work: sharing my story. Thank you to Dr. Robert Rogers, Master Jianshe, Judith Kahealani Lynne, Ruth McLoughlin, Amir Shah, Rene Kuiper, Dove Govrin, and posthumously to Bill Bulick, a treasured member of the Wisdom Healing Qigong community, who introduced me to Dr. Robert Rogers, who became my first mentor and supporter. Gratitude also to Ramon Testa and Daniela Carraro for translation efforts for my first book, *Reboot and Rejoice.*

Ongoing gratitude to Clare Henjum for your book editing, design and publishing guidance. Thank you to Isaiah Singer for your designs and support. You both bring professionalism, patience, intelligence, and skill. You are the ties that bind my work together.

And to my family: My son Aaron, daughter-in-law Kathy, and grandkids Emma and Alex, you so often provide the fun and normalcy that charges my battery. Keep it comin'. To my son, Justin, you inspire me. You were given a tough row to hoe with the autism syndrome, yet you continue to tirelessly work on yourself. How can I do any less?

To all my students and clients, current and former, I am grateful for the time and trust we share. Each of you enriches my life experience, and in so doing allows me to bring more to the table as I continue my work.

To Mother Nature, for providing so much breath-taking flora and fauna. The texture of my life is so enriched by my flowering plants and furry friends.

And to you, the reader. Thank you for your interest. May this book bring you beyond hope and into the world of recovery.

Introduction

*"I AM NOW ABLE TO SPEAK OF
PARKINSON'S IN THE PAST TENSE. I
WOULD LIKE OTHERS TO BEGIN TO
VIEW THEIR CHRONIC CONDITIONS
THROUGH THE SAME LENS."*
~Bianca

The further we progress in this journey of life, the
more we appreciate the significance of good health.
Yet, when we want our mind, body, and emotions to
heal, it can be difficult to find the time. But it can
be done, and I have written this book to help you do
just that, to make time to heal.

I invite you to open your heart and mind to the possibility that you have the time to change your health.

I was diagnosed with Parkinson's in 2008, and a little over a year later discovered the practice that healed me, Wisdom Healing Qigong. It is a mind-body practice designed to be gentle, yet powerful, as it gradually awakens the body's innate ability to strengthen and to heal. Unlike western medicine, where we take a pill or undergo surgery and then return to our fast-paced lives and hurried workouts, Wisdom Healing Qigong works to improve the flow of energy, or chi, in our body. This is not surgery, and cannot be accomplished in a matter of minutes or hours. Wisdom Healing Qigong requires daily practice to release old blockages and to prevent new ones from taking hold. We are working to maximize the open flow of chi or energy in our body.

PARKINSON'S, CHRONIC ILLNESS, AND PRACTICE

A condition like Parkinson's necessitates serious daily practice to expand the body's resources and re-establish efficient communication between body and mind. Parkinson's brought me to Wisdom Healing

Qigong, and on my journey I have now met people who do this practice for their cancer, Lyme Disease, chronic fatigue, and many other conditions. I have also met people in very good health who practice Qigong because they know it is key to maintaining their vitality and joy.

What we all shared in common was the commitment to joyful daily practice. For me that daily commitment was three hours. After a few years I was symptom-free and off my medications, and I remain that way today. I now consider myself one of those fortunate people who practices daily to maintain vitality, mental clarity, and joy. I am beyond grateful that the tremors, pain, frozen shoulders, foggy mind, balance, walking, and digestive issues of Parkinson's are all in the past.

Now I coach others in my consulting practice in the teachings and tools that helped me so powerfully. As with all new languages, subjects, and behaviors, learning Qigong occurs incrementally, and then one must Practice, Practice, Practice! This is where my students have the most difficulty. They find the learning phase is usually doable, but the practice is not. They are faced with common challenges to their commitment, and I have noted them in this book, along with suggestions and tips to keep the energy flowing.

My first book, *Reboot and Rejoice*, gives a general reflection of my own recovery process. *Make Time to Heal* is more of a practical blueprint on how to deal with the everyday challenges that arise in establishing a daily, dedicated qigong practice for both the newcomer and those seeking to refresh, extend, or deepen their practice. I have noted some of the most common challenges encountered in establishing a daily practice, as well as some of the "surprises" that occur along the way, surprises that can be misinterpreted because this type of healing is so foreign to what most of us have experienced to date. It is not a linear event, and does not appear as a steady upward linear ascent. "Appears" is the key word here. Through our Qigong practice, we learn to activate healing energy, and then allow it to do its job. Our homes may not always look their best in the middle of a remodel. Our bodies may not always look or feel their best in the middle of recovery. But in both cases, good, even wonderful, changes are happening. My simple, but not always easy-to-follow, advice, is to trust the process. The journey will undoubtedly take you to unexpected places at times. The more you learn about the process, the easier it will be. I am now able to speak of Parkinson's in the past tense. I would like others to begin to view their chronic conditions through the same lens.

WISDOM HEALING QIGONG

I have included a brief chapter on Wisdom Healing Qigong in case these teachings of movement, meditation, sound, and visualization are new to you. In this journey of mind, body, and heart, we connect with the inner self and cultivate the inner wisdom essential to healing. It works best as an unhurried process.

To heal from a major chronic condition requires time each day to practice, and the patience to continue with our mission over the span of months and, likely, years. I know the thought of spending so much time away from the busyness of daily life can seem intimidating. It is easy to become wrapped up in "doing" and to forget about "being." I recall the frequent panic-induced grip with which I clenched my car keys and the myriad sighs of frustration I would release each day. These were testaments to a life overtaken with responsibilities and to-do lists. I wondered how I could fulfill the practice requirement and decided I needed to try in order to find out. As my efforts began to have results, I had a reason to continue the practice. The healing journey of many of my clients, although always unique, has often included an onset of more calm and relaxation and joy. This relief encourages them to continue.

RADICAL CHANGE REQUIRES RADICAL ACTION

I have changed. Now my relationship with qigong, energy, and myself has transformed me to the point where I am doing more with less effort. Time does not wait for me, but now I work with it differently. This is what I would like to share with you, ways of working with time that are effective in establishing a successful daily qigong practice.

TIME

Give yourself the gift of time. The three hours a day I gave myself have changed the trajectory of my life. My tremorous, fatigued body had been on the road to nowhere. Now my healthy self ambles along the healing trail, slowly enough to be mindful of the beauty around me. I'm infinitely grateful for the time I spent working to recover, an investment far better than a lottery ticket.

Even though many of us will feel hurried to experience a change, please be open to savoring the practice and finding a new pace for your journey. So join me and let's discover how to Practice. Practice. Practice.

To continue exploring new pathways to wellness, you are invited to sign up for my blog at:
www.mettamorphix.com.

"MAKE THE TIME; ENJOY THE JOURNEY"

Haola, *(all is well)*
Bianca

CHAPTER 1
My Story

*"I GLADLY GAVE UP THREE
PLUS HOURS A DAY FOR THE
CHANCE TO RESTORE MY HEALTH."*
~ Bianca

We are sensitive beings, and long before we develop the language necessary to express our feelings, we are aware of them. Early on in our qigong practice we learn how the impact of emotions can affect the physical body. Powerful emotional events can contribute to blockages of energy, or chi, in the body. Old and new blockages can cause weakness and disconnection between mind and body, impairing the body's ability to heal and evolve. This process begins long before we can understand or explain it, from birth.

The miracle of life began for me in Queens, New York, in July of 1948. It was a hot, muggy summer and we lived in an upstairs apartment of a re-purposed mansion, one of many such dwellings common to post-World War 2 metropolitan areas. Dog days seeped into sweltering evenings at a time when no one had air conditioning and windows were kept open in the hopes of an errant breeze. And my parents had me, a squalling bundle of nighttime noise and vexation, and an invitation for a lynch mob if the windows were kept open. So Henry and Amelia Mollé opted to keep the windows shut, because I couldn't seem to do that with my tiny but booming infant mouth. And it turns out that the gas pains that had me squalling were diagnosed as colic, and then as an allergy to formula. So I was placed on a mixture of goat and soy milk. I understand that the soy fields back then were likely sprayed, and heavily so, with pesticides- one possible contributing cause for my later diagnosis of Parkinson's.

I survived the early digestive distress and entered into a fairly uneventful early childhood. I did notice that my family, first generation Americans, loved their Italian heritage and customs when they were together, but did not share this enthusiasm with the general public. It was right after World War 2, and it was best to blend in. Ethnicity could be a divisive factor. We needed to appear American on all counts. The surname Mollé was often mistaken as being French, and I noticed no one stepped up to correct the mis-impression when it occurred. I was named after my grandmother, Bianca, in Italian. The anglicized version was Blanche, and that was how I was generally known. Being a reflective child, I wondered about this and somehow felt a little shame about being who I was.

One thing I was not ashamed of was being a good student. I loved school and was proud of my performance there. It was fortunate that I didn't have to work hard for my grades, as my childhood was interrupted by my mother's terminal spinal cancer, which was diagnosed shortly after the birth of my baby brother, when I was seven years old. My mother began spending more and more time away from home, in the hospital. I gradually took on more and more responsibility. By the time I was in eighth grade I was cooking, cleaning, washing, ironing, waxing floors, caring for my brother, and achieving top grades with the expected regularity necessary to please everyone. And at the times when my mother was home from the hospital, I was responsible for bringing her the bedpan and administering carefully measured doses of morphine by injection. Giving a morphine injection was the last thing I did before leaving the house to ride with my neighbors to my Eighth Grade graduation ceremony; my dad was away on a business trip.

My mother died during my senior year of high school. I became a caretaker of my little brother, while my dad worked and travelled.

Later I went on to get my Masters in Education, got married, and started a teaching profession. All during this time my stamina and health were great. I lived a life like many did, finding ways to multi-task: being dedicated to my family, running the household, and teaching a classroom of children every day.

By the early 80's I became a single parent, raising two children, and working full time as a public school teacher. My youngest son was autistic and I learned to muster the extra energy and focus required to research treatments for autism. Eventually I found AIT, auditory integration training, and SIT, sensory integration training, both of which elevated Justin's functioning levels. When I later found Wisdom Healing Qigong, I saw the connection between Justin's therapies and my own, in that each utilized sound and vibration to achieve powerful results.

When I was diagnosed with Parkinson's, I realized my experience with my son actually helped me to be more calm. From the work I had done for my son, I knew I was already skilled in asking questions and exploring research that complimented conventional medical approaches. It sometimes takes a while to appreciate how life's most difficult lessons actually help us in many ways later down the road. But I am getting ahead of the story.

There is a sense of both contentment and gratitude I feel for where my life is right now. My family is in good shape, and I feel better than I have in well over a decade. The following describes a bit of where things were ten years ago.

In 2008, when I was diagnosed with Parkinson's, I remember leaving the neurologist's office shocked, but not surprised. The message from the increasing tremor over the last two years had tipped me off, despite my willingness to reside in denial. I was ac-

tually somewhat relieved by the diagnosis. It was an
explanation for so many of the difficulties, seemingly
unrelated, that had been insidiously creeping up on
me over the last decade or so: mysterious bouts with
"tendonitis" and "sciatica" which may have instead
been the onset of symptoms. Also, I had stopped
painting my fingernails several years earlier because,
unexplainably, the polish was finding its way beyond
the nail beds and charting a course to my upper
knuckles. Due to unsteady hands, I had stopped
wrapping gifts and used gift bags instead. Balance
concerns kept my mountain bike in the garage; stiffness kept me from yoga class. My fine motor skills
could no longer keep up with what were once simple
demands. In my classroom, I would try to conceal
my tremors from my students. My editing comments
on the student exams and reports became fairly illeg-
ible. Sleep was interrupted. Lower digestive distress
persisted. I see now that there was a cognitive decline
as well, which I only noticed and admitted much
after recovery. Mental sharpness retreats slowly and
surreptitiously, so it was difficult to detect and then
to acknowledge. Hubris went hand in hand with my
denial.

With my diagnosis came a set of prescriptive medi-
cines, including Sinemet, at times accompanied by

RerquipXL. There had also been a short and unsuccessful attempt with Mirapex. The symptoms were worsening, and the side effects of the medication were unwelcome additions to my already full agenda. This was not the direction I had planned for my life. Ever the researcher, my situation now motivated me to find a way to be free of Parkinson's and Parkinson's pharmaceuticals.

I found the Qigong practice called Wisdom Healing Qigong, taught by Master Mingtong Gu. I was surprised at how my body felt relief. I write about discovering this practice much more in my book, *Reboot and Rejoice.* Point of fact, I learned that this practice that was bringing relief to my symptoms, and giving me back a glimpse of who I really was, would necessitate extended daily practice.

I gladly gave up three plus hours a day for the chance to restore my health. The difficulties and challenges of my earlier life had imposed a powerful self-discipline. I was used to being the one laser-focused on the well-being of someone else. Now, after some self-dialogue, I had decided to do the same for myself. The process of a lengthy practice was no impediment for me, especially when combined with strong intention. Perhaps getting through some of the obstacles earlier in life had prepared me for this challenge. I think it may be helpful for others to reflect upon the difficulties they have already successfully navigated when charting their course for self-healing. They may discover that the necessary fortitude is already there.

One of the early questions, and often points of resistance, from new clients who seek my coaching advice, is a worry, and even a reluctance, about giving up time for practice. It does not surprise me, because the approach of western medicine has been to focus on quick fixes of symptoms, yet in Qigong we are exploring the roots of illness.

We bring to the practice our total life experience. We determine whether or not we are victims, whether an "obstacle" is a stumbling block or a stepping stone. Traumas become the raw materials from which we can begin to heal. Not by constantly dropping ourselves into the middle of past injuries, but by acknowledging they occurred and we survived. This validates our strength and encourages us to progress in our journey.

My story now includes my total healing from Parkinson's. Free of both Parkinson's symptoms and Parkinson's drugs, I now share this adventure by helping others. I coach people with Parkinson's or chronic illness on how to start and maintain a viable practice. I am also the author of the book *Reboot and Rejoice,* and travel worldwide and within the U.S. to introduce others to Wisdom Healing Qigong. I have truly learned that the receiving occurs simultaneously with the giving. I hope to give you some tools and inspiration so you, too, can derive the benefits of self-care, self-love, compassion for others, and the healing that can come from making the time to journey within. May you be well.

Haola

CHAPTER 2
About Wisdom Healing Qigong

"THIS BEAUTIFUL PRACTICE
RESEMBLES A GRACEFUL DANCE..."
~ Bianca

I will begin my definition of Wisdom Healing Qigong by explaining what it means to me. Somehow a New York-born gal, living in California, discovered a form of qigong created by a doctor in China, and it healed her from Parkinson's Disease. That means just about everything.

HOW I FOUND QIGONG

There is a saying: "Desperate times call for desperate measures." I didn't usually talk to myself, but, faced with a future of Parkinson's Disease, I gave it a try. Shortly after diagnosis, I had a conversation with Parkinson's, asking it to teach me. Fourteen months later the lesson showed up - in gold pajamas! Master Mingtong Gu appeared on the stage of the Marin County JCC, accompanied by his lovely wife, Lin-ling. The friend who had convinced me to attend this weekend workshop made sure we were there early enough to get seated near the front, to be close to the chi master. I could see the gleam in the Master's eye and feel the radiance of his smile. I will attempt to explain Wisdom Healing Qigong the way I remember hearing him explain it to me (and an auditorium full of people) on that day.

The golden pajamas were shiny, but not as shiny as the glowing ball Mingtong Gu used to illustrate his lecture on chi (energy). He explained that we are surrounded by all kinds of energy, healing energy among them. However, it is like we have a radio that is dialed in between stations, so what we experience is static. That is, until we use our intention to tune into the chi healing station, or Wisdom Healing Qigong.

WHAT IS WISDOM HEALING QIGONG?

Wisdom Healing Qigong is both an ancient and modern system of movement, meditation, sound, and visualization that instructs and guides us to open the flow of chi within our body, mind, heart and access the flow of chi that surrounds us in all life.

Wisdom Healing Qigong was developed by Dr. Pang, who studied nineteen mind-body chi/Qi disciplines and blended these teachings with his modern western medical training. Educated as a western medical doctor and doctor of Chinese Medicine, Grandmaster Pang opened the Zhineng Center, a "medicine-less center" in China, where he taught thousands of people these Wisdom Healing Qigong teachings. My teacher, Mingtong Gu, received the Master's Zhineng training with Dr. Pang.

Wisdom Healing Qigong is a gentle, moving mind-body practice that can be done by all abilities. It teaches us that through this opening and cultivation of chi, we can release blockages that contribute to and are caused by illness, stress, injury and aging.

There are three components of Wisdom Healing Qigong:

- **Cultivate.** It is learning and understanding we can cultivate the healing potential of our mind, body, and heart through these practices to feel joy, acceptance and to heal, even through the most challenging and painful episodes of life. (I did not know about qi or energy teachings, as it had not been present in my western learning curriculum, and so I started at square one.)

- **Practice.** We do our practice every day. My practice started at 3 hours/day.

- **Share.** Bringing blessing and gratitude to the world in our practice, and in our deeds. For me this last element is what encouraged me to become a coach to help others facing Parkinson's or a chronic illness. I still do my practice every day, and in every coaching session...in every interaction: buying bread or talking to my internet provider.

HOW TO LEARN WISDOM HEALING QIGONG

I learned this form of Qigong first from Master Mingtong Gu of The Chi Center, and also studied in China and internationally with other masters and teachers. I have attended some of Mingtong Gu's retreats, working with students with chronic conditions, and sharing my learning and practice tools.

Wisdom Healing Qigong is learned ideally through the guidance of a skilled teacher. It is more than simply doing the movements, even though this is where it starts, on the physical level. It is also carrying the experience into the emotional level. For people with Parkinson's, we have the added stress of getting through our day with a body and mind that are often fatigued. I had to retire from my beloved teaching profession earlier than planned because I couldn't keep up with the pace any longer. This was before I found Qigong. Now with Qigong I am back coaching and teaching without fatigue or other symptoms.

HOW TO DO A QIGONG PRACTICE

1. WE START WITH A CHI FIELD

The energy of our bodies reaches well beyond our physical form. When we intentionally create a chi field, we cast our net even further into energetic dimensions, connecting with other masters, teachers, and students. We are pooling our energetic resources and combining them with those of other practitioners, worldwide. We become energy magnets, drawing in healing energy. We connect with others who are doing the same. Being with a class or group, we often feel this connection at its most palpable. However, we connect to the chi field as well when we practice alone. That was most often my situation.

For me, setting a chi field marks the transition from my everyday life to the place where body, mind, and spirit unite. And through a dedicated practice in Qigong we are learning how to tap into and unite with the great healing chi field. This is where we need to be before we begin our practice. We close our eyes and place ourselves at the center of the universe, visualizing our head

touching the sky and our feet extending beyond
the earth, beyond the horizon, to infinity. We also
see our body extending in all four directions in
the same manner. Simultaneously, we welcome
all sensations, and feelings. We accept ourselves as
we are. We remember to include the planet Earth
and all life forms, and then we go deep into our
own bodies, inviting the chi to all organs, glands,
and cells. Especially because of my understanding of Parkinson's, I am now more aware of the
neurology of my body, so I go one step further
and include neurons, synapses, mitochondria,
and telemeres. We connect with the energetic
presence of the chi field, feeling grounded with
inner wholeness and harmony. We are at one
with all of life. We then place our hands over the
navel, women right hand first, men left. Usually
we close our eyes at the start of this exercise and
open them after we remove our hands from the
navel at the conclusion of chi field creation. There
are some slight variations for setting the field, and
you may come across some. It's fine. Healing is a
creative process. The idea is to reach out to to the
healing energy field, expanding, and then to focus
on going inward.

2. WE DO THE MOVEMENT/ MEDITATION/SOUND

The Wisdom Healing Qigong practices include movement, sound, meditation, and visualization. When I work with my clients, I coach them in these practices and sequences that fit their needs. These practices can be done sitting, standing or with visualization while lying down.

I receive numerous requests on a regular basis, asking me to recommend the best Wisdom Healing Qigong practices for Parkinson's. These are some of the practices that I like to use:

LACHI

Lachi is the simplest Wisdom Healing Qigong practice, and illustrates the basic principle of all the practices: energy in, energy out, or "open/close".

We are seated with back straight, elbows out, and movements are generated from our shoulder blades as we open and close our hands, which have palms facing each other, about 6 inches apart. Think wingspan. This is often challenging for someone with stiff or frozen shoulders. Additional support can be provided by relaxing the elbows atop cushions or pillows when you start this practice. Gradually challenge yourself from there.

Close your eyes and envision a ball of light between your hands. As you open your hands to expand further, another few inches on each side, visualize the light diffusing, like sending out rays of sunshine, then, as you bring your hands back to their original, closer position, envision the light now becoming more concentrated. Keep repeating this movement, along with the word "kai", meaning "open", and "hui" (pronounced similar to "huh"), meaning "close."

Inside that lovely ball of light you can envision your intention for health, happiness, whatever you are working on.

There are stories from the times of Dr. Pang's medicine-free hospital, of people arriving who had very little movement and could only do lachi practice. With perseverance they were gradually able to achieve more movement and progress to other practices.

LIFT CHI UP POUR CHI DOWN (LCUPCD)

This beautiful practice resembles a graceful dance, but without the fancy footwork. That was one of its initial draws for me. My balance was off, feet a bit stiff, and I was having memory challenges. Here my feet didn't need to remember to do anything. And there is logic to the movements.

In Phase 1 we draw in energy first from in front of us, then from alongside us, and then we go down into pump/squat, coming up to connect with the heavenly energy above us.

In Phase 2 we draw in the energy alongside us first, then from in front, then repeat the squat/ pump and connecting with energy above.

For Phase 3 we draw in energy from behind us on the left, then the same from the right. This final phase involves no pump/squat, but instead lotus hands and a final dive upward into the chi field above.

The *Lift Chi Up Pour Chi Down* practice has over 90-odd individual movements, but many are repeated through each of the three phases, so it starts to become familiar quickly. Luke Chan's book, *101 Miracles of Natural Healing*, has each movement sequenced in photographs, frame by frame, at the end of the book.

That, plus using select Mingtong Gu's Chi Center learning video materials, usually 3 times daily, is how I memorized this practice. I also encourage you to take the time you need practicing with the video instead of setting out to memorize the *LCUPCD* practice from the get-go. It is key to let your mind rest from trying to remember the sequence and to relax into the practice. You will learn the practice over time, and it is much more important to focus on the energetic healing process than to memorize the movements. That will come with time and patience.

AWAKENING PRACTICES

The *Awakening Practices* are simple, gentle movements, often easy to learn on the physical level, but one must also be conscious of directing energy though visualization, meditation, as well as movement. The *Awakening Practices* are *Lachi, Chen Chi, Spinal Bone Marrow Rotations, Hip*

Rotations, Bending Spine and Wall Squats. These movements are not calisthenics and should not be practiced as such. We are connecting body, mind, and spirit here, as we do the movements.

The *Awakening Practices* are very good for the beginner student, and often seem more familiar to people who have done yoga, plus they help with strengthening core and reshaping posture, areas of great benefit for the Parkinson's practitioner.

STANDING MEDITATION

Standing Meditation is a valuable, centering, Wisdom Healing Qigong Practice. I do this practice following *Lift Chi Up, Pour Chi Down.* The *Standing Practice* has no movement. You are standing with feet about shoulder-width apart. Hands are cupped around navel, fingers framing it and pointing downward. Imagine energy entering from yong quan (soles of feet) first, then from the bahui (top of head, fontanel area), then envision the human energy from your heart. See all three energies converging at the dantien or inner core, behind navel.

With *LCUPCD* you have invited and drawn in external healing energy, and with *Standing Meditation* you are directing it throughout your body.

SOUND HEALING

We know that sound, in the guise of music, can be soothing, even healing. We know that sound energy vibrates. *Wisdom Healing Qigong Sound Healing* is an ancient tradition with sounds being passed down for generations. Traditional Chinese Medicine comes from the standpoint that most disease is caused by energy blockages, and that we process emotions energetically through our organs. When we make the prescribed sounds, three for each organ, we set energy in motion, pulsing through the organs. Thus we are offered the opportunity to emotionally clean house. And the lovely benefit of using *Wisdom Healing Qigong Sound Healing* is that each organ has three sounds, representing the physical, mental/emotional and spiritual levels. As once stagnant energy now courses through the body, healing begins to occur. By making the sounds we are transforming the negative emotion to its positive counterpart. Daily repetition is the best way to support the practice.

A chart of all the organs and their accompanying sounds can be found in my book, Chapter 7, of *Reboot and Rejoice*, as well as in the *Sound Healing Technologies* book and CD by Mingtong Gu from The Chi Center, so I will not list all the information here, and will simply provide examples. For instance, the lungs are the organs that process grief, loss, sorrow, and depression. So when we make the three sounds for the lungs we are working to transform sorrow and depression to equanimity and joy.

When I first began the practice, after a few weeks of daily *Sound Healing* and *LCUPCD*, I was definitely feeling more energy, and a bit less pain, stiffness, and constipation. Already I felt less "sick" than I had in recent years. Yet I had developed a deep, loose cough which sounded terrible. I couldn't understand what was happening because at the time I didn't understand how Sound Healing worked. I didn't realize that my lungs were recovering both from the unprocessed grief of my mother's death when I was seventeen, and from the smoking habit I picked up for a time when I was in college. So I just kept on practicing, coughing, and expectorating for about four to six weeks. I continued to feel better and better in the process.

The best part about *Sound Healing* for me was that I got to develop a new relationship with my body. For most of my life, the focus was on my brain. I dragged my body around like excess baggage. It was fun to dress it up, feed it well, and to hike or swim with it, but beyond that I really didn't think much about its contents. Now, I was spending time with each organ, visualizing it, becoming aware of its function and assigned color. My organs began to claim their rightful place in my priorities, and more and more I began to feel the results of positive transformation. I was becoming healthier and happier. Also, my old notions of perfectionism began to dissipate. I knew there was no way I could make the sounds exactly like the master, so I just did my best each time, not allowing frustration to invade. I remembered that Mingtong had said that intention was much more necessary and powerful than perfection, and my intention was very strong.

Another benefit derived from this practice was that my voice was returning to its full potency. When I began *Sound Healing*, I couldn't hold the

sounds and had to keep taking breaths to follow
along. Little by little that changed. Eventually I
was able to belt out the sounds and sustain them
along with the recording. Beyond that, for the
first time in many years, I could sing "Happy
Birthday" at parties and actually hear myself,
instead of the curious silence that used to appear.

3. WE CLOSE THE PRACTICE

As we close the practice we gradually transition
back into the world. We place our hands over
the navel, men left hand first, women right hand
first. We make a gentle bow as we give thanks for
doing this practice. We gradually open our eyes
and reintegrate back into daily life, refreshed and
energized.

WHY LIFT CHI UP POUR CHI DOWN?

For me this practice connected on a deep level.
Looking back, I now realize that I had been extreme-
ly stressed and anxious most of my life. So from
childhood on, I believed what I was experiencing was
normal. Kicking back, chilling out, relaxing, were
not in my repertoire. The 30 minute experience of
LCUPCD took me out of that anxiety zone. I knew

that several, usually three times per day, this practice, with its slow movements and mellow music, would provide me with solace and relief. I got to spend blocks of time with myself, for myself. I was on a cloud of comfort.

VISUALIZATION

I am often asked how I visualize while performing *LCUPCD*, so I'll share a bit here, while reminding you once again that healing is a creative process and you are welcome to individualize. Speaking of creative, there is a wonderful book, *Sacred Mirrors*, by artist Alex Grey, which Mingtong Gu often uses to illustrate the energetic body. You may want to take a look there as well.

THINKING IN SPIRALS

Ancient shamans observed nature and from there derived that energy travels in spirals. Quantum physics agrees. (Think DNA and some planetary movement). So when visualizing, see energy entering the body through the energy gates of laogong, palms of hands, and yong quan, soles of feet. These are also known as "bubbling springs."

PHYSICAL RESTRICTIONS

Chronic illnesses, and especially Parkinson's, can limit mobility. Wisdom Healing Qigong was developed by a medically trained physician to accommodate people with challenges that might limit their ability to sit, to stand, or to move their limbs. Physical limitations need not be a drawback as each practice can be modified, done from a chair, or simply visualized, depending on circumstances.

MUST I STAND FOR STANDING MEDITATION?

No. It can be just as powerful from a chair. As I was healing from PD, my legs and feet were often swollen and painful. At times I was in an orthopedic boot. I would stand for *LCUPCD*, but by the time that was over my legs and feet needed a rest. So I sometimes sat for this standing practice. Remember that healing is about self love. It's ok to be kind to yourself.

THE BUTTERFLY METAPHOR AND ENERGY

The transformation of caterpillar to butterfly imagery is a beautiful representation of the energetic healing process. And we can extend the metaphor further when we practice. During one wonderful lecture in China, Master Gu encouraged us to see ourselves as caterpillars. In that way we had hundreds of hands (what would be caterpillar feet) extending out from our bodies to draw in chi.

Again, these are all simply suggestions for the many who may be discouraged about their ability to visualize and therefore dubious about the effectiveness of their practice. I have a good imagination in a number of areas, but I don't consider visualization one of them. When I first began practice I doubted myself here, but kept on plugging. I was surprised that someone as unskilled as myself began to see results. It gave me the confidence to carry on. So keep your strong intention and keep going: "Fake it till you make it."

WHEN AND WHERE TO DO SOUND HEALING PRACTICE

I realize we are all busy and like to maximize our time on the road. I am often asked about using the Sound Healing CD (from The Chi Center) while driving. Sorry, but no. To derive maximum benefit from the practice, I close my eyes and visualize each organ bathed in its corresponding color and think about its function. I attempt to devote 100% of my attention to it. I lay down and place a scented weighted eye pillow across my face. I always attempt to put my all into this practice, and multi-tasking is a diversion. I give this practice it's full due.

Although there is no way to measure, I consider Sound Healing to be at least 50% responsible for my recovery. The time and attention paid to the inner workings of my body changed my feelings about it from frustration and resentment to gratitude and appreciation.

'MAN'S MUSIC IS SEEN AS A MEANS OF RESTORING THE SOUL, AS WELL AS CONFUSED AND DISCORDANT BODILY AFFLICTIONS, TO THE HARMONIC PRO-PORTIONS THAT IT SHARES WITH THE WORLD SOUL OF THE COSMOS."
~ Plato (Timaeus)

CHAPTER 3
Attitude

*"WE MUST ACCEPT OURSELVES WHERE
WE ARE, AND GO ON FROM THERE."*
~ Bianca

Why would a *time-themed* book devote a section to attitude? Because you waste your time if you don't bring your best attitude to the practice. I have seen many people become harsh self-critics because they don't perform the moves identically to the master or teacher. They forget that they are here to work on themselves, not to compete. They have not yet learned that self-love is an essential aspect of healing. You do the best you can with your body, and what your body can't yet do, you allow your mind to visualize. We must accept ourselves where we are and go on from there.

OPENNESS AND ACCEPTANCE

Acceptance is where we must be to start our practice. We bring our complete selves to this work, tremor, stiffness, fatigue, and all. It is not always easy. I needed to remind myself of the loving acceptance shown to my autistic son, Justin, even when he was perseverating or tantruming or exhibiting some other oppositional behavior. Now I had to deliver that same loving acceptance to myself, a feat far more challenging. Embracing myself as I am, tremor, unsteady gait, stiffness, whatever had become my new reality, I reminded myself that I am the same person as the one in that adorable baby picture, all dimples and smiles. I'm the same person who educated herself and had a successful career. I'm the woman who longed to be a mother and then nurtured two boys to manhood with love, joy, and usually, confidence. I'm the same person who can genuinely love family, friends, and students, no matter what their condition. So now I need to love myself. When this happens I begin to want to work for me, to do what it takes, to practice Qigong for three hours a day. I would devote three hours a day to support a loved one in need; now I do it for myself. I'm worthy.

FAMILY SUPPORT

The family network can be both a wonderful thing and also a challenge. I have encountered those with totally supportive spouses or partners, oftimes practicing together. This is ideal. At the other end of the spectrum, I have seen some hide their practice from meaningful others rather than deal with anticipated negativity. Sometimes it is because others may be singular in their devotion to the western medical approach, and find this "energy/Qi" practice just too new and unusual to give it a try.

I remind my clients that we are working here with energy, where openness and expansion are both goals and rewards. That's hard to do when attempting to keep the practice under wraps, especially if one is motivated to conceal their Qigong activity by negative emotions like fear and anxiety. We empower ourselves when we work on healing, not by disregarding the notions of others, but by explaining what we are doing and inviting inclusion, without expectation. If they join us, fine. If not, we carry on. We can hold the intention of change as we practice, continue to surround the partner in a vision of love, and see what happens over time. In other words, have patience.

It's great to get support from your family, but you must be ready to take this journey alone. Hopefully, they will see the changes and honor your practice time, and maybe even join you. Be prepared to continue on your own. Ask your family to allow you this journey, and when they are testing you for linear results, remind them that this Qigong work is like preparing to run a marathon, this is a practice that peels away the onion layers of many years of living and attitude, so you can cultivate your own joy and resilience. I have met wonderful people who are doing Wisdom Healing Qigong to improve their aging, mental clarity, or to deal with chronic illnesses like Parkinson's, Lyme's Disease, cancer and more. Through our common study of this form of Qigong, I now have people I can reach out to ask questions and get abundant support.

I will add that in my experience it is so much more beneficial and nurturing if family can accept, and certainly not demean, a person who is exploring the role of energy in their health journey. I started years ago, when little of western medicine was recognizing these ancient teachings, and yet now they are catching up in their research. More and more conventional medical centers are now adding meditation, yoga and Qigong to their patient's wellness protocol. For many of us with PD, we can't wait for science or our friends and family to catch up, and for us, we are finding the teachers and feeling the results.

BRING JOY TO YOUR DAILY PRACTICE

"HAPPINESS IS A CHOICE.
NOT A RESULT"
~ *Ralph Marston*

I found in Qigong many things I hadn't realized were missing. It was like all my life I had been driving around, looking for a spiritual parking spot, but none quite fit till I came to this practice. This brought happiness and a sense of fulfillment. Almost every day I felt a little better, and on difficult days I reminded myself of how far I'd already come. I was better than when I started, and if healing progressed no further, I was still better than before I began the work. That thought brought me joy, and I found myself playing my favorite tunes and dancing around the living room on a regular basis. Oddly enough, on those occasions my body seemed totally Parkinson's-free. If we remember that joy and healing occur at the same vibrational frequency, it is not surprising at all. Bring joy to your daily practice.

PATIENCE

> *"PATIENCE IS BITTER,*
> *BUT ITS FRUIT IS SWEET"*
> ~ *John-Jacques Rousseau*

We live in a world of rapidly increasing pace and demand. Communication has become instantaneous, travel is often lightning swift with rapid transit and smart trains, monetary transactions can occur within seconds, we often forget that:

> *"THERE IS MORE TO LIFE THAN*
> *INCREASING ITS SPEED"*
> ~ *Mahatma Gandhi*

Our Wisdom Healing Qigong practice is our opportunity to slow down both the body and the mind, to allow them the chance to reconnect. This is why, although it is great to learn the moves and be able to practice independently, I encourage people to remain with the support materials I provide or recommend to make sure they are going slowly enough. Then they may want to challenge themselves by moving even more slowly.

Also, we must have patience with ourselves and the work we are doing. Many of life's beauties have a gestation period of sorts: humans, animals, plants, learning and understanding concepts. Think of your healing practice as having a gestation period of its own, an as yet unknown interval. Don't have preconceived expectations, especially for instantaneous results. Step into the flow and go where it takes you.

GRATITUDE/APPRECIATION

There is often a distinction made between gratitude and appreciation. Gratitude is more general in scope, and can include appreciation under its umbrella. Appreciation is more specific and doesn't have to include gratitude. I am grateful for both my children. I appreciate the unique qualities that make each of them who they are. I am grateful for my home. I appreciate the colors and forms that surround me. I am grateful for my recovery from Parkinson's. I continue to appreciate all of the Qigong practices that got me there. Both sentiments are healing and wonderful.

As I continued with my practice I found not only gratitude for my ongoing healing, but also discovered a new appreciation for all that surrounded me. I began making mental lists at the end of each day for all I appreciated. This was a far better exercise than taking my worries to bed, as I had in the past. Later on, long after I'd healed, I read in numerous places that gratitude and appreciation are important parts of a healing practice. And appreciation becomes its own reward, as the flowers that I once barely noticed appear shockingly bright and vivid now, and my capacity for joy can be triggered by the sight of a squirrel or hummingbird outside my window.

Not all my thanks is for the good and the beautiful. I realize that life's challenges are opportunities for me to expand my practice, my equanimity. I must admit I was doing pretty well with this aspect until the results of the 2016 U.S. Presidential Election were tabulated. In this area I'm still a work in progress, reminding myself not to become energetically engaged with the current divisiveness. I speak my truth, but attempt to do so with equanimity and compassion (and an occasional cuss word). I'm still working on transforming anger to equanimity. It's a daily job. But I'm grateful for all the wonderful people I've met at rallies, protests, and town halls. I'm grateful for compassion and positivity that also shows up at these events. And I appreciate that because of my Qigong practice, I have the resilience to march, and stand, and chant and sing for extended periods of time at these gatherings. I remind myself that this is not the first time I've been singing "We Shall Overcome." I remember the words of Oscar-winning screenplay writer of "*Moonstruck*":

> *"I WOULD LIKE TO THANK
> EVERYBODY WHO EVER PUNCHED
> OR KISSED ME IN MY LIFE AND
> EVERYBODY WHO I EVER
> PUNCHED OR KISSED."*
> ~ *John Patrick Shanley*

In Qigong we recognize and embrace the role of our attitude, in who we are and how we can heal. In *Sound Healing* we chant three sounds, the first is to open the physical body, the second sound opens the mind/emotional body, and the third the spiritual body. This is because from the Qigong perspective, for every illness or injury there is not just the physical response, but the emotional response, and we embrace that true and lasting healing shall include all levels. So for example, for someone feeling anger, perhaps from their diagnosis, pain, or world events, we look to bringing relaxation to the liver organ, and transform this anger into courage and righteous action. We need an attitude of courage to commit to our daily Qigong practice, because it is not just one time we do the practice to heal, it is an ongoing commitment.

I have seen my attitude shift over the years to where I have so much more openness and resilience and joy than from before I ever started my PD symptoms.

DEDICATED COMMITMENT

Finding time to practice is your job, this is not a hobby when you are healing. It takes priority. Most of us can't afford to take time off from work because we are not feeling motivated on a particular day. We remember our commitment and the reward that often comes from our work. It is the same here. A cavalier attitude does not serve well. It is possible to discover a new resilience and focus, especially through the distractive mind of PD, and multitude of medical appointments that occur.

WHAT IS THE ROLE OF INTENTION IN MY PRACTICE?

Intention is the cornerstone of Wisdom Healing Qigong. We are consciously training the mind to focus on parts of the body, emotions and energy that many of us have never been trained to do. Through this mindful practice we direct our mind to these areas in need. It takes practice. Some days it is easier than others. I have found a new mental clarity that gives me focus and energy to last much longer each day.

WHAT KIND OF EXERCISE SPACE AND AND CLOTHES DO I NEED?

The great gift of Wisdom Healing Qigong is that special clothing or mats are not used or needed. I do recommend comfortable clothing, so you can move with ease. You need just enough room to move your arms freely, bend, etc. It is valuable to turn off phones, so your practice is not interrupted. If possible, select an exercise space where you can close the door, turn off the phones, and relax. If you have more than one person doing Qigong, then be sure to adjust the space, so you are all free to move. In addition, this form of Qigong was designed to accommodate people with health and physical limitations, so the practices can be done standing, but also sitting or lying down. Visualization is an important part of Wisdom Healing Qigong for everyone, and a key component for people experiencing mobility challenges.

RELAX FROM THE TO-DO LISTS

I have become more aware of the lifetime of *To-Do* lists I have made, and somehow bonded myself to complete. For many years prior to my healing, numerous times throughout the day, I heard myself sighing in exasperation and fatigue. My life was a long *To-Do* list, and for every item checked off, several new ones appeared. That modus operandi allowed little space to notice all that was working well in my life. Such an attitude is a prison of sorts, and one I am pleased to have deserted.

COMMUNITY

In practicing Wisdom Healing Qigong we are connecting with an entire community. Openness and acceptance of ourselves and others is required. And both the community and the practice itself supports and encourages us to reach out. This is so important for those with chronic conditions who often isolate themselves. Here we can make chi buddies and practice together, even long distance via computer or phone. The whole is greater than the sum of its parts, and we benefit from the powerful connections we make.

"LIFE HAS NO REMOTE. GET UP AND CHANGE IT YOURSELF."
~ Mark A. Cooper

CHAPTER 4
Practice Time

"LIFE IS NOT A RACE, BUT A JOURNEY."
~ Bianca

When people read my story, they are sometimes intimidated by the fact that I practiced a minimum of three hours a day for several years. To anticipate the question of how long I now practice, today I spend about half that time in formal practice, but much of every day beyond that is spent in instructing or advising around the qigong practice, plus I incorporate mindfulness of chi into just about every waking moment. I'll give some tips on how to do this at the end of this chapter.

I DON'T HAVE TIME TO PRACTICE, HOW CAN I FIT THIS INTO MY SCHEDULE?

So what made me decide I could do it: spend three hours or more, each and every day, in practice?

The answer is very simple: I wanted to heal and would do whatever that required.

The weekend that I was introduced to Wisdom Healing Qigong, Master Mingtong Gu suggested three hours of daily practice for anyone working with a serious chronic condition. The thought of this much practice felt very foreign to me, and at first I was, frankly, annoyed. Then logic took over. If pain and fatigue were limiting me to the sofa for eight to ten hours most days, what if I spent three hours with qigong practice and then had the energy to begin re-entering my life?

It was worth a shot, and cost me nothing but the price of CDs and DVDs, classes, and, of course, time. I had plenty of time since I was newly retired from teaching, reluctantly leaving my classroom due to the pain, tremor, and fatigue of Parkinson's.

My motivation level was strong. I had recently been blessed with grandchildren and had a vision of being active with them. Both my grandmother and mother had spent a good part of their adult lives as invalids. They were given attention and treated with love, but eventually their condition removed them from the forefront of the family. I was not yet ready to "go gentle into that good night", nor was I comfortable with "rage" as the poet Dylan Thomas suggests. I just wanted "normal"- no trauma, no drama, just the ability to carry on in a way that I had once taken for granted.

NOT EVERYONE EXPERIENCES PAIN WITH PARKINSON'S

Not everyone experiences pain as a symptom of Parkinson's. It is a small fraction of PWP's who encounter this, Central Pain Syndrome. I note this because often when I'm speaking publicly and mention my experience with pain, there are a few relieved audience members. Like me, they are sometimes told there is no pain with Parkinson's. My neurologist went one step further and said it was probably depression and sent me off to the psychiatrist, who tested me and decided I wasn't depressed, but genuinely in pain. Fortunately for me, a few days later I found Wisdom Healing Qigong.

WHAT ABOUT TIME AND MONEY, FAMILY AND SOCIAL OBLIGATIONS?

There is another aspect to the "no time" issue that I have observed first in myself, and now as I work with others. What about family, friends, co-workers, obligations, finances? Well, what about these concerns if the Parkinson's continues to progress?

Often people delay starting a program that could help them recover their health because they are wary of making the commitment. So they waste time getting started. When looking at energetic healing, one must take the long view. And re-organize priorities. Healing yourself is currently your main work. There is usually some price to pay. An example occurred when I made the decision to attend my first retreat.

My first retreat occurred several months after being introduced to Wisdom Healing (Zhineng) Qigong. It was held in China. Prior to any of this, my family and I had planned a Yosemite vacation. I was going to spend a week of quality time with my older son, his wife, the grandkids. Now this idyllic vacation was in conflict with the healing retreat.

I felt torn, but took the long view. I wanted my loved ones to have the healthiest possible me for the longest possible time. I told myself I could do Yosemite another summer. I knew this was my healing time, and entered into the flow of that concept. Here's an update: I haven't yet been to Yosemite, but have no regrets.

I'M JUST RESISTING PRACTICE, EVEN THOUGH I ENJOY IT. WHAT CAN I DO?

And there is another aspect of resistance to practice that sometimes emerges, disguised as not having time. I have found that people with chronic conditions are often kind, loving, and patient with everyone but themselves. At times they don't like themselves very much, sometimes due to difficulties separating themselves from the condition. Two suggestions for dealing with this:

- Treat the condition like a visiting professor. It has come to teach you much about yourself, self-compassion, and self-love.

- Make a list of things you like about yourself. If this assignment is too difficult to start with, list what others like about you. Keep expanding the list.

Now, for those tips on how to keep mindful of your qigong practice when in the midst of daily activity:

1) I admit to being a San Francisco Giants fan. That's a lot of baseball television viewing time. During commercials I mute the sound, close my eyes, and do a gratitude/appreciation practice. Here's an example: "I am grateful for: my passion for baseball, the gift of sight I use to watch the game, the will, focus, and determination of these athletes which inspires me to continue and intensify my own qigong practice."

2) Another way to handle those commercials is to mute the sound and do a few minutes of hip rotations or some other preliminary practice. This is an informal practice, as one has not established a chi field. However, it's health related movement, so Haola!

3) I replace invading negative or stressful thoughts with "Haola" and silently chant "Haola" when walking from parking lot to supermarket, waiting in line at the bank, etc. ("Haola" translates into - "all is well and getting better" - and invites the intention of acceptance and health into

every cell in my body; repeating it as a mantra can be a practice in itself.)

4) I replace watching network news (too sensational) with PBS news broadcasts. When a reported item is just too tragic or heartbreaking, again I mute the sound and do lachi/fachi practice sending loving energy to those involved.

I WORK FULL TIME. HOW CAN I DO THIS?

What about those working full time? Qigong practice can bring benefit to your physical self and your professional self as well. I suggest starting with a minimum of an hour to an hour and a half each day, and then setting aside long blocks of time on weekends and days off for practice. Learn all the *Awakening Practices* so you can have a portable repertoire to take along with you wherever you may go.

I like to start people with *Lift Chi Up Pour Chi Down* practice because it is a long practice with many slow movements, giving plenty of time to switch out of stress mode and into the relaxed yet energized state that qigong creates.

You will discover that you can find the practice time in your day for Wisdom Healing Qigong because:

*"TIME IS ON MY SIDE
WHEN I'M ON MY SIDE"*
~ Bianca

CHAPTER 5
Meditation and Distraction

"WE ARE ALL MAD HATTERS,
OVERSCHEDULED, OVERWORKED,
OVERWROUGHT..."
~ Bianca

Time in the moment can be a stressor unless we learn to step back and adjust. In our Western dominant culture, products and productivity involve a timeline and measurement. We are all Mad Hatters, overscheduled, overworked, overwrought. This constant and considerable stress is a major catalyst to developing chronic health issues. Then, when that happens, we are asked to take time out and virtually do nothing (meditate). This is a dramatic change, and one that is necessary if we are to restore our health.

THE IMPORTANCE OF MEDITATION

In a 2014 Harvard University study the benefits of a mindful meditation practice were demonstrated. Here is an excerpt from an article on the study:

> Test subjects taking part in an 8-week program of mindfulness meditation showed results that astonished even the most experienced neuroscientists ...The study was led by a Harvard-affiliated team of researchers based at Massachusetts General Hospital, and the team's MRI scans documented for the very first time in medical history how meditation produced massive changes inside the brain's gray matter.
>
> Although the practice of meditation is associated with a sense of peacefulness and physical relaxation, practitioners have long claimed that meditation also provides cognitive and psychological benefits that persist throughout the day.'...The participants spent an average of 27 minutes per day practicing mindfulness

exercises, and this is all it took to stimulate a major increase in gray matter density in the hippocampus, the part of the brain associated with self-awareness, compassion, and introspection... 'Participants reported reductions in stress were also correlated with decreased gray-matter density in the amygdala, which is known to play an important role in anxiety and stress. None of these changes were seen in the control group, indicating that they had not resulted merely from the passage of time.'.. 'It is fascinating to see the brain's plasticity and that, by meditation, we can play an active role in changing the brain and can increase our well-being and quality of life.' (Source: Lambert, Brent, see Chapter 10: Resources for information)

I HAVE TRIED TO MEDITATE NUMEROUS TIMES AND FAILED. MY MIND JUST CAN'T BECOME STILL. WHAT CAN I DO?

Peace is here for all of us, we simply need to discover how to cultivate it. That's no easy task. We are told that meditation and being in the moment are keys to personal health and harmony, yet that darn old monkey keeps clanging those cymbals inside the head.

You know the imp that I'm referring to: our "Monkey Mind": The creature that makes you compile a grocery list or reminds you of that unanswered email, when you're attempting to connect your inner being

 with universal source energy. It is tempting to give up in utter frustration, thinking "I'm just someone who can't meditate."

I found myself there many times, and learned to simply smile and mentally wave goodbye to the invading thought, and get back into the moment until the next disruption occurs, often following along rather quickly. So then I just repeat the process. And instead of seeing the exercise as a failure, I remind myself that I'm human, pat myself on the back for my continued efforts, and carry on. Perfection is by no means a requirement. Sustained effort is.

SHOULD I GIVE UP? I DON'T FEEL I AM FOCUSING DEEPLY

I know there are people who go into meditative states and have all sorts of cosmic experiences that sound wonderful, and maybe even a bit scary. This has not been my experience. Maybe I'm still on the bottom rung of the meditational ladder, but I've learned not to care that the heavens don't open or that I'm not receiving flashes of colors that I didn't even know existed.

I have had a daily "sitting" practice for nine years now, and the cumulative effect is one of increasing calm and joy, not to mention health. I remember that intention counts very heavily, and my intention to meditate is clear, strong, and focused. It outweighs any distraction or lack of mystical experience. I have learned to be confident in myself and my best efforts. And my efforts have not gone unrewarded. Besides grocery lists and emails, creative thoughts and even problem solutions sometimes appear on my meditational vision screen now. It is known that composers and other creative types often receive suggestions when in dream state. I'm wondering if this is a similar phenomenon.

Part of the list-making and other distractions can arise from some subtle, even undetected sense of guilt: How can I just sit or lie here, taking time out, when there is still so much left undone? And there is so much hype, all true, about the value of movement in working with Parkinson's and other chronic conditions. So the temptation may be to set aside the meditation for cycling, walking, jogging, etc. After all, we equate activity with productivity, even if this isn't always so.

The key is to find a balance. Even more importantly, remember that Wisdom Healing or Zhineng Qigong is always a meditative practice, even when doing the moving practices. The slow movements help reconnect the body and brain, retraining and re-introducing the body-mind relationship. And focusing on the movement gives the mind a direction so there is less room for Mr. Monkey and his clanging cymbals.

WHAT ABOUT BEING DISTRACTED BY PAIN AND DISCOMFORT WHILE TRYING TO MEDITATE?

It is often suggested to breathe into the pain. I can now do this a bit more successfully than several years ago, but in my advancing studies of qigong I have learned a tip from my teacher, Master Mingtong Gu, that I'd like to share. During stillness, ask yourself where your body is holding pain, both physical and emotional, and send energy to those places. Relaxation is key here.

As you begin, relax yourself from head down, noticing where tension is held and letting it go. Often shoulder or abdominal tension is observed, but it can be anywhere. Continue working down to the feet. Now, do this again, visualizing energy moving through your body from the head down. Stop at the places where you feel discomfort and visually send energy to that part of yourself. Continue with this for as long as you like, then, when finished, slowly move your body.

The above exercise shows how any stumbling block can become a stepping stone. If you're emotionally upset, use the moment to feel where this affects you physically and meditate there. Instead of abandoning or pushing away the practice because of a sudden upset, find a way to use it to pull the practice into your life whenever possible.

WHEN WE HAVE LESS TIME TO PRACTICE

I realize that we do not always have the luxury of a half hour for meditation, so here are some suggestions for when we have less time:

- Scan your body for tightness. Are your shoulders up to your ears? Relax them. Exhale.

- Put a smile on your face and keep it there. This action gives your body chemistry the message that all is well.

- Try self-hugs. This posture can be accomplished without fanfare and gives the body a safe secure feeling which then informs the mind that all is well.

- Visualize all your organs and cells inside you smiling.

- Have some short meditation recordings handy on your phone.

- Breathe in golden chi, slowly and deeply. Breathe out gray, spent energy.

- Do some lachi with positive intention, Lachi is a movement and meditative practice in Wisdom Healing Qigong that focuses on opening the heart. Include positive intentions, such as: Visualize a vacation, staycation, daycation - ie: Get yourself into pleasure mode by thinking about what pleases you. Going into reward mode can help encourage dopamine.

- Actually do something that pleases you: play music, have a cup of tea, go for a walk or drive in nature and notice all that is beautiful around you.

- Appreciate all that is lovely. Anxiety and appreciation cannot share the same space. You are the proprietor of your mind. Keep out the riff raff.

- If you are too antsy to sit still for a sitting meditation, you can always choose a physical Qigong practice, depending on how new you are to the practice. Make sure your movements aren't frenzied calisthenics. You may want to try a few minutes of Iachi/meditation first to get yourself in slow-down mode.

I work with my clients to find the practices that allow them to find time in the moment. They are the pilots, charting their healing course.

"THE BAD NEWS IS TIME FLIES. THE GOOD NEWS IS YOU'RE THE PILOT"
~ Michael Althsuler

CHAPTER 6
Dealing With Anxiety

"ANXIETY IS THE RAW MATERIAL
THAT WE CAN SHAPE INTO A
USEFUL DEVICE. IT'S ALL ABOUT
TRANSFORMATION."
~ Bianca

We can have anxiety in our life for many reasons, and with a chronic illness like Parkinson's it can become a part of our experience. There is currently a TV commercial broadcasting in the United States that has done a grave disservice to many persons with Parkinson's. It shows scenes from everyday life, but a bit dreamlike. The narrator explains that he has Parkinson's and sometimes cannot differentiate between reality and hallucination or delusion. The commercial gives the impression that Parkinson's Disease is what causes this psychosis. That can be true. That can happen. But what the commercial doesn't tell you is that there are many medications, Parkinson's and others, that are also likely culprits: "The medications most often associated with visual hallucinations include those used to treat high blood pressure, erectile dysfunction, psychiatric and mood disorders, movements disorders like Parkinson's Disease, and some antibiotics." Dr. Frederick W. Fraunfelder, quoted in American Academy of Ophthalmology article titled: ("Medication-Related Visual Hallucinations: What You Need To Know", March, 2015)

EMPOWER YOURSELF

So why am I introducing a chapter that addresses anxiety with a paragraph about hallucinations? Because I have seen what that cruel, unscrupulous, and alarming commercial can do to someone with Parkinson's - create anxiety to the point of immobilization. Stressing a person with Parkinson's into more immobility is not healthy.

My suggestion is to mute the commercial, turn your eyes away, and implement one of the anxiety-reduc-

ing tips listed further along in this chapter. You don't
have to roll with the anxiety-producing commercial.

What exactly is anxiety for a person with Parkinson's? It is all too often an ongoing symptom of the
condition. This makes sense considering the gloomy
prognosis Western medicine provides. So, for many,
anxiety is the Bogeyman, lurking under the bed and
in the dark corners of the mind. It has a snowballing
effect in that left unchecked, it becomes bigger and
moves faster. The fear factor of anxiety can certainly
be a negative. Physically it can manifest as palpita-
tions, nausea, dizziness, headache, chest pain, neck
tension and more. For a person with Parkinson's who
may already be having mobility challenges, the onset of an anxiety event can be one more reason to sit
still, becoming slothful in body and mind. For anyone a sedentary lifestyle can be unhealthy, but with
Parkinson's it is imperative that we move the body
and remind our mind to connect with every muscle
and organ in the body.

Wisdom Healing Qigong is training us to realize that
anxiety is an energy to be transformed. It becomes
the raw material of healing. TS Eliot informs us that:
"Anxiety is the handmaiden of creativity." How many
times do we hear from someone receiving an Os-

car or some other award that they are trembling? A
certain amount of anxiety reflects for us that we are
alive and vital. Too much can immobilize, weaken,
and sicken. There is a matrix here, and working with
confidence in our own powerful minds and energy,
we can begin to control the degree of this experience.

If we practice treating anxiety as a passing cloud and
wave goodbye, as we do with distracting thoughts
that interfere with our meditations, we may be surprised, over time, to find that tranquility has been
patiently waiting for us. The further along I go on
this journey, the more I observe that things that once
sent me into a tailspin no longer do. Whether the
situation involves the electrician about to quote me a
price for rewiring my home, or the unmindful free-
way driver who cuts me off, I marvel that my body
no longer contracts with fright and that my mind
now remains open and clear. These response tools to
anxiety didn't happen all at once, but gradually. It
started to happen as soon as I began my dedicated
practices of Wisdom Healing Qigong. The key to
Qigong is regular, continual practice. It is through
my first 100 day Gong that I noticed incremental
increases. (A gong is a 100 day practice. A particular practice or practices are selected to be completed
each day, along with a particular time frame set. This

is to be done faithfully, daily, without skipping. If one day is missed, we practice double time next day. If we miss more than one or two days, we must start again at day one.)

It has been my experience and opportunity, in working with clients, to be present and supportive when they are in the midst of an anxiety event. I guide them in a reflective process to put the brakes on anxiety, by immediately going into meditation. I find that a sound meditation works very well here. Besides engaging the mind, it occupies the body as well, because of the vocalization involved. Over a half-hour period of meditation I have watched the countenance transform from worried and constricted to clear, open and peaceful. With every incident, we are developing new skills to transform our lifetime 'surrender to anxiety' and to instead surrender to meditation. In place of following the trail of one worry to future negative "what if?" consequences, we take the road less travelled through meditation to calmness and peace.

> *"CHOOSE TO BE OPTIMISTIC.*
> *IT FEELS BETTER."*
> ~ *Dalai Lama*

WHY DO SOUND HEALING FOR ANXIETY?

In western medicine and culture we often want the anxiety to stop, to simply go away. Many people resort to medications to dull its effect. In Qigong we learn to transform the fear into alertness. We aren't making it vanish but are allowing the parts of anxious fear that can serve us, allowing the traits of alertness and determination to emerge, so our well-being is nurtured. First responders will certainly feel fear when they see a fire, but it is their ability to redirect that fear into being alert so they can safely and quickly enter the building to save a child. In Wisdom Healing Qigong we learn the sacred sounds that are connected with key emotions and the body organs. Emotional health is a cornerstone of Wisdom Healing Qigong, and integrated in the meditation, sound and movement practices. This is especially beneficial for the person living with Parkinson's, because there are many emotions that emerge in response to this diagnosis and the intense physical effects on the body.

MORE ABOUT SOUND HEALING

When in private, my go-to method of anxiety reduction is *Sound Healing Practice*. The calming effect of this practice has been noted by just about everyone I've worked with. I have watched facial and bodily appearance relax after students complete the practice. Remember that in Traditional Chinese Medicine the kidneys are the organs that process fear, and the adrenal glands sit atop the kidneys. So my visualization during this sound healing practice includes the kidneys and adrenals. Here's where creativity and fun come in. Since the color for the kidneys is dark blue or black, I picture my kidneys as twin baby boys, swaddled in blue buntings and relaxed in fetal position. They wear red knit caps to represent the adrenals. You are intentionally focusing the gentle and kind power of the mind to these organs and glands, rather than trying to ignore and run away.

HAOLA: ALL IS WELL

Parkinson's presents itself in the mind, heart, and body in perplexing ways, ways that can make it difficult to remember tasks, to move the body, to believe in the possibility of healing. And to complicate the matter, in Parkinson's, when anxiety appears, it can be accompanied by physical symptoms such as nausea, dizziness, increased tremor.

Whether your condition is Parkinson's or something else, please don't give it too much power. Numerous times I have heard from clients: "I have Parkinson's and anxiety is a symptom" as if this explains that nothing can be done. Yes, anxiety occurs, and like stiffness, tremor, fatigue, etc., it is a symptom which you can work to mitigate. Don't allow anxiety to become your personal Bogeyman. Don't become attached to it. Maybe you have felt anxiety episodes since childhood, from before you had a Parkinson's diagnosis, and feel it is embedded in your genetic code. Through a practice in Wisdom Healing Qigong, we learn we can release these patterns, even after decades of that type of response. You are invited today, to get that smile in place, take a deep breath, and remain in the moment. Think of how in this moment "All is well." Stay in the moment. Don't visualize catastrophe; instead use your mind to visualize peace.

ASSUME LEADERSHIP

When I relate my story of healing from Parkinson's, I relay how I actually spoke to the condition within me. Remember that I had lived a traditional life as a school teacher. I was not a CEO or business magnate. Yet shortly after diagnosis, and prior to discovering qigong, I had a meeting with my mind-body-spirit committee. I can remember my words: "Ok, Parkinson's, I'm a teacher and this is a teachable moment. I'm open. Teach me!" Yes, it was a command. I was in charge. The same technique can be used for anxiety. Think of it less as a dangerous stranger and more as a longtime associate. It has been a part of you; it can't be all bad.

ABOUT ANXIETY

The reason I describe anxiety as a longtime associate is that, looking back on my life, I become aware that anxiety was with me from my earliest memories. The atmosphere of my mother's extended suffering with cancer hung over my childhood for many years. Anxiety was pretty much my second skin, but I had no idea anything was off. Some researchers claim that physical or emotional trauma in childhood can be a contributing factor to Parkinson's Disease. It doesn't mean one had to grow up in a war zone, though that has happened for far too many. It doesn't mean there had to be one huge identifiable incident or event. It can be more like a chronic looming dark cloud overhead, filled with concern over an absent or ill parent, perhaps worry over the health of oneself or a sibling, worry over basic necessities, perhaps social apprehensiveness, or numerous other causes. Different people process these events differently, which partially explains why you may experience the anxiety to greater degree than a sibling or someone else in similar circumstances.

I think it's important to note that for many with Parkinson's, although anxiety may have been with us a long time, sometimes, via adrenalin boosts, it has served us well: increased creativity, heightened awareness, increased productivity-the ability to shift into overdrive. Many people with Parkinson's are over-achievers and have done quite well for themselves professionally. We never hear complaints about this. So if anxiety has been a constant companion, then releasing it 100% is neither advisable or possible. And, I think, to some, it may unwittingly be so familiar that it is simply allowed to take over, as it did in childhood, with no attempt at control. Instead, through a dedicated Qigong practice, we cultivate a capacity to pause, so we can stop, check in with ourselves, see how we feel. If the anxiety level is useful, no need to do anything. If the physical symptoms begin to overwhelm, or thoughts are going to the dark side, STOP. Take a breath and decide how you want to "change the channel." It is natural and normal to fear the enemy. But anxiety need not be the enemy when we claim our own power and relax into it. Anxiety is the raw material that we can shape into a useful device. It's all about transformation.

So that nasty commercial may be misleading, but it is true that hallucinations or disorientation may appear. If, for any reason, that occurs, please check in with your physician.

None of the advice given here is meant to replace or change medical treatment or therapy. It is simply offered as a suggested support, because just knowing these tools are available can provide some relief. Through my practice of Wisdom Healing Qigong, I have expanded my capacity to calm my anxiety, and have a softer response to stress and worry.

"LIFE IS TEN PERCENT WHAT YOU EXPERIENCE AND NINETY PERCENT HOW YOU RESPOND TO IT."
~ Dorothy M. Neddermeyer

CHAPTER 7
Practice Tips

*"ALLOW YOURSELF TO FALL IN LOVE
WITH THE PRACTICE AND THE REST
WILL TAKE CARE OF ITSELF."*
~ Bianca

This chapter provides additional tips for your daily dedicated practice. I am providing some common questions that I receive from my conferences and clients.

WAS MY THREE-HOUR PRACTICE SESSION ALL IN ONE BLOCK EACH DAY?

I am often asked this question by my readers and clients. The answer is almost never. For me, 30-40 minute blocks at various times throughout the day worked well. As I began to feel better I returned to the classroom to substitute teach, so I learned to fit the practice into my new work schedule. Occasionally, when I had a free day, I'd do several hours at once. It was lovely, an in-home retreat.

I suggest that some weekends be set aside for an in-home retreat. Ideally you could practice either with a chi buddy, if not in person, via Skype or Facetime. I guide a practice with clients, and it can be a wonderful motivation to follow through on the intent to schedule in more practice.

A GLIMPSE AT MY DAILY PRACTICE

My practice has changed from when I first started, to what I call my maintenance program. Initially it was three or more hours everyday without fail. After my recovery, I stayed dedicated and modified to a maintenance program that I find continues to keep me symptom-free, and it has a goal of two hours. I also coach my students and lead them in practice, so this adds more practice time.

First thing in the morning is always the best time to start. I find that many of my clients are hit with anxiety upon awakening. I, myself, like to begin the day with a short *Lachi* meditation, even before I get out of bed. Then I recommend one of the *Awakening Vitality Practices* upon standing. These basic or *Preliminary Practices* (called *Awaken Vitality Practices* at The Chi Center), include: *Spinal Bone Marrow Rotations, Hip Rotations, Chen Chi, Bending Spine, Lachi, Wallsquats.* They are all wonderful practices and can be fit into whatever time frame you have available.

Later in the day, when you have more time, I recommend *Lift Chi Up Pour Chi Down* (approximately 30 min), followed by *Standing Meditation* (approximately 10 min.) if possible. Although some may question the idea of scheduling a beginner with with 30-40 minute blocks of practice time, I think it allows one to go deeper and stay longer in the chi field, the healing place, thus treating the body/mind to a preview of what can be experienced on a more regular basis. I find it motivational.

I strongly believe *Sound Healing* should be included in each day's practices. It addresses the emotions which are often working overtime when faced with a chronic condition. Much more is said about *Sound Healing* in the Wisdom Healing Qigong chapter. Suffice it to say, it's important.

The complete *Five Organ Sound Healing Practice*
takes about 30-40 minutes. *LCUPCD* followed by
Standing Meditation takes another 30-40 minutes,
plus the ten to twenty minutes of morning lachi/
awakening practices will bring you to an hour to an
hour and a half practice, a good way to begin your
first week of qigong. Please note, you are always welcome to do more. I did.

HOW CAN I STAY MOTIVATED?

- **Practice with a coach consultant.**
  I often hear from people who want to learn
  and develop a practice in Wisdom Healing
  Qigong and would like coaching guidance
  through the process. I teach them the movements, meditations, sounds and visualizations,
  and customize the learning steps to fit their
  individualized needs. Guided practice is a really good way to transition into the practice and
  the community. Also, sometimes all it takes is
  one individual session to get someone off to
  a well-informed start. I also hear from people
  when they want to work with me to prepare
  for attending their first Wisdom Healing Qigong retreat, and also as follow-up to maintain

their learning and practice specific to their goals and conditions.

- **Commit to a 100 day gong.**
  This means selecting a practice and an amount of time, and doing it faithfully for 100 days. Keep notes if you like. It takes just about that amount of time to establish new habits, and to re-train our neural pathways. My initial 100 day gong was to do three hours of Wisdom Healing Qigong each day. You can contact me via my website (www.mettamorphix.com) and I can send you a 100 DAY GONG SHEET that you can print and use to track your practice.

- **Join a local or online Wisdom Healing Qigong (*Zhineng*) Qigong class.**
  Teachers and classes can be found online, and also at many local community centers and even medical centers. I co-teach a weekly class at Kaiser Permanente, for example. I suggest you look for a Wisdom Healing Qigong class, as there are many Qigong forms.

- **Create a Practice Place**
  Find or create a quiet space for your practice.

Especially in the beginning, this space would include a DVD player, CD player, or whatever technology will allow you to watch or follow along with the teachings while doing your practice. Make it a spot you'll enjoy, comfortable and visually pleasing.

- **Make Time**
  Make sure to start your day with some practice- either when you get out of bed, (even while still under the covers for meditation and lachi) or after breakfast, depending on digestive requirements. I like the afternoon for sound healing as I get to relax in the middle of the day. So suit yourself as far as which practices you do when, and rearrange if you need to freshen up your practice. Just do the math and make sure you're getting in lots of time, or whatever your 100 day Gong commitment was.

  My suggestion is to try Wisdom Healing Qigong practice for three months, actually 100 days, and then determine if you want to continue. During that amount of time, with a dedicated daily practice of at least three hours, you will be able to ascertain benefit and decide if you want to continue.

You can contact me via my website and I can send you a 100 Day Gong Sheet at www. mettamorphix.com. I used this during my first 100 days, and never looked back, except to see Parkinson's in the rearview mirror.

- **Relax**
  Another reason to practice first thing in the morning is to replace the anxiety many people with Parkinson's feel upon awakening with a positive, healing activity. Persistence here will pay off.

- **Enjoy**
  Allow yourself to fall in love with the practice and the rest will take care of itself. One of the great pleasures I have in my coaching work is introducing people to this beautiful practice and sharing in their joy as they begin their journey into the chi field. Usually there is a sense of inner calm that either presents itself as an old friend returning or a new and welcome companion. Often that new sense of well

being is reflected even in appearance: a more joyous and radiant countenance.

CHAPTER 8
Healing Chronology

*"THESE ARE NOT THE HEALING
OLYMPICS. THERE IS NO PRIZE FOR
GETTING AHEAD OF ANYONE ELSE..."*
~ *Bianca*

The above quote sounds completely counterintuitive, especially to those diagnosed with a condition defined as chronic, incurable, and progressive. We are already feeling imprisoned in an uncontrollable body, and now we are put in an even smaller box, one containing no hope.

So often when people come to qigong, they bring with them a sense of urgency. They feel that they must hurry up and heal and beat the ticking clock. I was contacted by someone wanting a "quick fix" from Parkinson's. To my knowledge, no such thing exists.

Energetic self-healing via qigong requires a daily dedicated practice. And again, as mentioned earlier, one must take the long view. If you try to measure gains after each practice, you'll not only drive yourself crazy, you'll most likely slow the progress that could be happening.

Why? These are not the Healing Olympics. There is no prize for getting to the finish line ahead of anyone else, and because we are all unique, each individual may have a different finish time and finish line. To perceive healing as some type of competition is to add unnecessary stress and anxiety, the same factors that helped bring on the condition. It is beyond counter-productive. It is downright harmful.

HOW DID I VIEW MY HEALING PROCESS?

When I noticed I was beginning to heal, as energy increased and pain and other symptoms gradually abated, I met each day with joy and hope. Because I had not heard of anyone else who had completely healed from Parkinson's, I did not hold an expectation of becoming completely healed. Yes, the thought of full recovery was in my consciousness, and the ultimate goal, but I was simply grateful for gradually feeling better, and told myself each day that if the healing progressed no further, I would be grateful for the recovery I'd already made.

Furthermore, if my recovery began to unravel, I would be grateful for the time of respite I'd had from full-blown symptoms. Looking back, I now see that I did not set up a conflict in my healing process. I was always pleased with where I was, I was not struggling to beat the clock, or someone else's healing record.

This is why I am reluctant to answer the frequently asked question: "How long did it take you to heal?" With a broad brush stroke, the answer for me was roughly two plus years for physical symptoms. The tremor was the last to go, and lasted long after other symptoms had disappeared. It had gotten to the point where I thought it could be permanent.

But I was so pleased to have energy, digestive regularity, legible penmanship and to be free from pain,

slow walking, occasional foot drop and foggy thinking, among other things, that I was fine with the
remaining tremor. I was not angry with myself, nor
did I consider my endeavor a failure, and I did not
isolate myself as damaged goods because of sometimes noticeable shaking.

Please remember this as you do your work. You
are working with a condition that took years, even
decades, to develop. It is unlikely to disappear over-
night. And some symptoms take much longer than
others to abate. The secret is to stay positive, enjoy
the progress to date, and don't try to compete with
my, or anyone else's, timeline.

I will share with you some of what was going on in
my head as I experienced partial healing. First off, I
was grateful for the healing that had occurred. That
in itself was a miraculous surprise. Then I looked at
my tremorous hands and appreciated the many years
they had served me steadily, efficiently, skillfully.

I was reminded of the years I spent in Special Education, of the many brave and spirited students I'd
worked with who didn't know life without a wheel-
chair, walker, or some sort of physical or sensory/
cognitive assistive device. These boys and girls are my

role models. These everyday heroes faced each day with courage and humor. They taught me as much as I taught them. They accepted their situation and so I learned, years later, to accept mine. Fully healed, partially healed, it didn't matter. I was on a course, headed in the right direction, with no idea about where the road ended. Healing is about the journey.

WHAT ABOUT WHEN SYMPTOMS SEEM TO INTENSIFY OR RE-APPEAR?

This is all part of the healing process, often called chi purification or reaction. Dr. Constantine Hering, a 19th Century homeopath, had nothing to do with Qigong. He did observe the healing process, and what he observed is also known in allopathic medicine as the Hering's Law of Cure. This phenomenon notes initial healing and improvement, followed by what looks like a return of the disease or some of the symptoms. It is basically a deeper detoxification that is occurring. These reactions may last a few days, weeks, or longer.

Here is an excerpt from an article discussing the Hering's Law of Cure and the healing process:

> ...when proper treatment is used, one may well re-visit symptom patterns from an earlier

stage (of one's life - when the disease patho-
genesis was being formed), to the extent that
those symptoms were not resolved (i.e. healed)
at the time, or - as is commonly the case -
were suppressed by previous treatment proto-
cols. This is the principle of reverse progression of symptoms, which (in an uninterrupted
period of holistic healing measures) will
continue until all the unresolved disease conditions are resolved, going back even to early
childhood. Herings Law provides a symptom
hierarchy - a way to assess the course chronic
disease is taking, i.e. towards healing, or towards deeper manifestation of disease.

The concept of the healing process related to
chronic disease is an interesting, and insightful
aspect of natural therapy. Of course, it runs
contrary to the basis of allopathic medicine, so
many in the medical community may reject it.
The reality is that it will also not be accepted
by many people because in comparison to the
apparent quick-fix of pill-popping remedies,
its time-consuming, and demands an active
participation in measures to regain health and
well-being. It is a marathon, not a sprint.
Not everyone will take up such an approach,

but we do believe that everyone should know about it. It can be a life changing paradigm shift that applies the principle to their self-healing endeavors...

And what about the movement back to genuine healthfulness? Take someone with asthma (or another lung imbalance). If the condition is regressing (i.e. genuinely getting better), then in the course of reverse progression of symptoms, it's quite possible that a skin imbalance (such as eczema) or a bowel condition (such as IBS-like symptoms) may show up. At the same time, despite the recurrence of these symptoms, the general trend of the person's thinking and emotions is positive and hopeful. All of this is indicative of healing: the course of the disease is going from inside-out (e.g. internal toxicity expressed as eczema/IBS-like symptoms), greater to lesser organs (lungs to skin), from top to lower down (chest to the abdomen); in reverse order of symptoms formation (bowel disorders typically precedes asthma type symptoms, but are often not recognized as a real problem at the time); general improvement in the headspace (positive thoughts, clarity of thinking, feeling alive, hopeful, better moods, glad to be alive, sense of resilience). *(Excerpt from Julia Chappell, Right Healings: Hering's Law of Cure, p 2-3)*

For me, my healing process was increased tremor and, to a lesser degree, pain. I would think this cycle had abated and then it would re-emerge. As I recall, this often happened when I was in an excitable state, positive or negative, and whenever I was in the neurologist's office. Also, several times I experienced what can only be described as a "whole body tremor"- my legs shook so much that my hips were also shaking. This had not been a part of my regular Parkinson's experience before starting with Qigong, so I'm guessing it had to do with healing, because it went away.

Also, a few times during practice I almost fell over backwards - long after the balance issue had abated - it felt a bit like being pushed from the front. Another odd thing was that as I was healing, a tremor appeared in my right arm, which had not been noticeably affected prior. Others I have worked with have had tremor and stiffness and fatigue come and go.

One of my clients, after several years of daily dedicated practice, has shown many signs of healing, including restored facial expression and sense of smell, less shoulder stiffness, improved digestion and skin condition, better balance and walking. There are times when fatigue and slowness are increased. This is not regarded with alarm. This practitioner is aware and grateful for the improvements to date, and remains positive about the situation. The positivity and clear-headedness with which she views her progress are likely the catalysts for her continued ongoing healing.

Not all reactions are physical. This is wholistic healing, and emotions are involved. As we clear out negative emotions, when this occurs intensely, we can feel a bit overwhelmed. As we work with Qigong and especially sound healing, the blockages of energy in our body open up and release. This can result in a release of emotions that have been suppressed. Through Qigong we learn to note unpleasant thoughts and feelings as they make their exit, and to not dwell on the story. This has been my experience and that of many I work with. My clients have many emotional stories that they are carrying, as we all do. They also often share in common the emotional response to getting the diagnosis of a chronic condition. Of course, if the story is very powerful and/

or you have challenges with depression, please be mindful to talk with your support team and medical professional.

In most situations, the Qigong practice will open these energy blockages, and start the healing process. With every practice we have the opportunity to exercise ourselves as healers. Some suggestions that can help are:

- **Chi Rain**

  I use this visualization, that I call Chi Rain, to transform negative thoughts and feelings to positive. Imagine chi raining down from the heavens, appearing like a vertical line "|". It intersects with the negative thoughts which appear as a horizontal line "—". The resulting symbol, when these two marks combine, is a plus sign "+", literally transforming negative to positive.

- **Self-Hug**

  Dr. Kristen Neff, Ph.D. founder of self-compassion.org, speaks about an intense flood of detoxification as emotional backdraft, and suggests self-hugging as one way to reset body chemistry.

- **Relax**
  Relax. Breathe. The intent here is to always be gentle and kind to ourselves in this journey, as there is no hurry. And as your equanimity returns, return to your regular practice.

The trick is to keep swimming in the ocean of chi instead of diving into the sea of despondence. Don't allow your mind to play tricks on you. You know when you've been healing. Don't negate all the good that came before because you are now at a challenging point in the process. Ride it through. Practice more. Treat yourself well. Find pleasurable activities. Stay positive.

The above is all speculation from a non-medical person, me. I am in no way suggesting that you avoid your doctor. Just be aware of how the healing process can appear and remember this information when you share your situation with your physician.

HOW DID YOU REMAIN CONFIDENT THAT YOU WERE HEALING WHEN YOUR TREMOR INCREASED?

A major question for many people is about tremor. Many note that when they first come to Qigong their tremors seem to increase, especially during practice. Students need to understand that energy vibrates along with the tremors, which facilitates healing. It can turn one's perspective on its head to view increased tremor as a good sign. Somehow it's liberating. So they learn to respond to tremor differently. Qigong masters sometimes have visible movement of hands when practicing, from the strong vibration of energy. My clients cultivate new skills to embrace tremors as energy movement in the body. Often they find that at other times their bodies seem more still.

I can't promise the total release of all symptoms, but I can share that for me the tremor was the last symptom to go, and that I have consulted with several others very far along in their healing process who are currently left with little else but tremor. Time will tell how much further their healing will take them. It is clear they don't regret the hours spent in practice each day.

It didn't make sense to me that the tremor symptom was progressing because so many other gains remained in place. My facial expression, penmanship and gait held their ground, my shoulders were flexible again, constipation gone. My inner voice continued to affirm all was well. So I was not very concerned with these short visits from former symptoms.

And when I noticed tremor for the first time in my right arm, I told myself the disease was going in fast forward, working its way through and out my body. I see now how fortunate I was to have held that perspective. It is difficult to learn to trust in oneself to the point where you view yourself as capable of creating healing. A challenging day, or period, can be enough to set someone into a tailspin.

So chi purification, or Hering's Law of Cure, coupled with the fear that re-visiting symptoms are permanent, can appear to stall the healing process. I think this is often what happens when people experience a plateau in their recovery. My only advice here is to be patient, especially with the self.

*"HAVE PATIENCE. ALL THINGS
ARE DIFFICULT BEFORE
THEY BECOME EASY"*
~ Saadi

WHAT IF I FAIL?

Since energetic healing has its own timeline and process, I don't know how failure fits into the concept
with this work. Perhaps total healing isn't what will
occur for everyone, but most who start the practice
do at least feel a sense of calm, and can progress from
there. If physical symptoms don't reverse, it is not
failure. Who knows at what point in time this could
happen?

It doesn't mean one is practicing wrong, isn't motivated enough, is not worthy. Here I can use myself as
an example. I was able to heal from Parkinson's and
titrate off all Parkinson's meds. After that I was able
to eliminate statins, anti-anxiety, anti-depressants,
and anti-allergy medication.

However, I've had a high blood pressure condition
since my late twenties, and have been on medication
for it for about forty years now. I have read stories

and witnessed people come off their hypertension meds after a short time with qigong. This had not yet happened for me. I have had several conversations with my doctor about it, as well as tried on several occasions, with motivation and diligence, to address this with Qigong. I can get it down for a short time, but the meds provide the steady pressure readings necessary.

I will continue on medications until I get some indication, like low blood pressure readings and light-headedness, and then check in with my doctor before doing anything with meds. I do not consider myself a failure. I am working with my body and the conditions it holds, doing my best to be responsible, love myself, and stay positive.

I am grateful that at my age, with a family background of hypertension and coronary disease, to be taking a fairly low dosage of only one medication. I don't feel or think of myself as being limited in any way by this condition. The way I see it, by a certain age almost everyone has developed some type of condition, dues we pay for our time on the planet. I continue to work daily on my health, and am OK with the fact that my healing endeavor is less than perfect.

> *"GIVING UP IS THE ONLY SURE*
> *WAY TO FAIL"*
> *~ Gena Showalter*

CHAPTER 9
Conclusion

*"LOVINGKINDNESS IS PART
OF THE QIGONG WAY."*
~ Bianca

I wrote this book to help me remember the healing process, and to share it with others. Once the outcome of my practice cultivated results for me, I forgot all about any suffering inherent in the process. This healing journey from Parkinson's was much like natural childbirth. While I was immersed in it, it had my attention. Then when my children arrived, I was filled joy and appreciation. The same is true with my

healing journey. I wake up everyday filled appreciation, and do not fixate on life's struggles.

IN A HURRY

I had to learn how not to hurry. I had hurried to
do my tasks since I was a young child. Through my
practice I have learned to slow down. As that occurs,
I notice more. I notice how being first, or at the
top, is a goal for some people. And they bring this
egocentric notion to their healing practice. I quickly
divest them of it. Ego is what makes people try to
compete in "The Healing Olympics." Again, think
about labor in childbirth. Some labors last an entire
day, others a few hours. Yet both mothers are experiencing the birth process. We are all different. The
best mother isn't necessarily the one who delivers
first.

HUMILITY

There is a certain hubris about thinking it is necessary to be better or do something better than everyone else. Always use your best effort and forget
about the others. Appreciate yourself and those who
support you. The less hierarchy the better. Ego can
present as the rigid dictator who tells you not to be
happy or satisfied unless every last vestige of every

symptom is gone. Being in the present tells you to celebrate where you are now. There is always a reason to be grateful or appreciative. Focus on what is going right and the rest will fall into place.

LOVINGKINDNESS

Lovingkindness is part of the Qigong way. If we are truly compassionate with ourselves and others, we are not concerned with competition or one upmanship. If we want more healing, we simply do more practice. Your journey up to this point was unique, and so your healing journey will also be unique.

COMMUNITY

You can do this practice on your own, but many of us realize deeper benefit from the guidance of a teacher, especially in the early stages. In addition it is both enjoyable and valuable to do an occasional reboot with a teacher, with a friend, or in community with other practitioners at a class, workshop or retreat. As with most learning experiences, the sharing of ideas and activities brings a fresh look and new enrichment to the practice. In addition, the experience of chi can be amplified in a community setting or with a trained teacher.

SHOW YOURSELF SOME LOVE

The ego can put one at odds with self compassion. Lovingkindness, especially toward self, is a main ingredient in the healing formula. It is part of the recovery remedy. To my knowledge, overdose is not possible. So show yourself some lovingkindness and practice, practice, practice.

"QIGONG MEETS YOU WHERE YOU ARE - RIGHT NOW, FOR THIS DAY AND THIS MOMENT, TO CHANGE WHAT IS POSSIBLE IN THE STEPS AHEAD."

~ Bianca

CHAPTER 10
RESOURCES

This chapter features an alphabetical listing of resources you may find helpful. This includes teachers, authors, books, websites, and other materials that have in some way, either directly or indirectly, informed the contents of this book.

People and websites

Bianca Mollé, M.ED, Mettamorphix: Provides individual coaching services to help people cultivate a practice in Qigong through chronic illness, including Parkinson's. www.mettamorphix.com

100 DAY Gong Sheet at www.mettamorphix.com: This chart helps you track your daily practice to both encourage your dedication, and also track the changes over the weeks, months and years of practice. Please contact Bianca Molle for a complimentary chart at www.mettamorphix.com.

Linda Graham, MFT, https://lindagraham-mft.net

Mingtong Gu, The Chi Center and Center for Wisdom Healing Qigong, Galisteo, NM
www.chicenter.com

Kristin Neff, Ph.D, www.self-compassion.org

Robert Rogers, Ph.D, https://www.parkinsonsrecovery.com

Books and Related Resources

Achor, Shawn. (2010) *The Happiness Advantage: The Seven Principles of Positive Psychology that Fuel Success and Performance at Work.* Publisher: New York, Penguin Random House.

Chappell, Julia. *(undated) "Right Healings: Hering's Law of Cure".* Posted at www.westlondoncolonics.com

Chodron, Pema. (2002) *Comfortable with Uncertainty: 108 Teachings on Cultivating Fearlessness and Compassion.* Publisher: Boston and London, Shambhala Publications, Inc.

Chopra, Deepak, M.D., and Tanzi, Rudolph E., Ph.D. (2012) *Superbrain Unleashing the Explosive Power of Your Mind to Maximize Health, Happiness, and Spiritual Well-Being.* Publisher: Ebury Publishing.

Dispenza, Joe, D.C. (2007) *Evolve Your Brain: The Science of Changing Your Mind.* Deerfield Beach, Florida, Publisher: Health Communications, Inc.

Doidge, Norman, M.D. (2016) *The Brain's Way of Healing: Remarkable Discoveries and Recoveries from the Frontiers of Neuroplasticity.* Publisher: New York, New York, Penguin Books.

Doty, James R., M.D. (2016) *Into the Magic Shop: A Neurosurgeon's Quest to Discover the Mysteries of the Brain and the Secrets of the Heart.* Publisher: New York, Avery, A Division of Penguin Random House.

Elgin, Duane. (2009) *The Living Universe, Where Are We? Who Are We?, Where Are We Going?* Publisher: San Francisco, CA, Berrett-Koehler Publishers, Inc.

Goswami, Amit, Ph.D. (2004) *The Quantum Doctor: A Quantum Physicist Explains the Healing Power of Integrative Medicine.* Charlottsville, VA, Publisher: Hamptom Roads Publishing Company.

Grey, Alex with Ken Wilber, Carlo McCormick. (1990) *Sacred Mirrors: The Visionary Art of Alex Gray.* Publisher: Inner Traditions International

Gu, Mingtong. (2013) *More Energy, More Life: The Lift Chi Up, Pour Chi Down Method.* Publisher: The Chi Center.

Hawkins, David R., M.D., Ph.D. (2002) *Power vs Force The Hidden Determinants of Human Behavior.* Publisher: Hay House. First published in 1985.

Jahnke, Roger, OMD. (2002) *The Healing Promise of Qi: Creating Extraordinary Wellness Through Qigong and Tai Chi.* Publisher: Contemporary Books.

Lambert, Brent. (2014, November 19) Harvard Unveils MRI Study Proving Meditation Literally Rebuilds The Brain's Gray Matter in 8 Weeks. Publisher: *Feel Guide*, Retrieved from https://www.feelguide.com/2014/11/19/

Mollé, Bianca, M.ED. (2013) *Reboot and Rejoice: How I healed from Parkinson's Disease using the body/mind method practice of Qigong.* Publisher: Mettamorphix Press.

Moorjani, Anita. (2014) *Dying to Be Me, My Journey from Cancer to Near Death to True Healing.* Publisher: Hay House

Rankin, Lissa, M.D. (2014) *Mind Over Medicine: Scientific Proof That You Can Heal Yourself.* Publisher: Hay House.

Wade, Mary, Contributing Writer, Interviewing Frederick W. Fraunfelder, MD. (2015, March), Medication-Related Visual Hallucinations: What You Need to Know. (Retrieved from www.aao.org)

Quotes:
In gratitude to people who bring hope and insight to others through their words, the author included quotes from inspirational writers and speakers, that she has used for her own wellness journey in this book. You can find these quotes on such websites as: www.goodreads.com, www.brainyquotes.com.

"FOR THE TIME OF YOUR LIFE,
GIVE YOURSELF SOME TIME TO
PRACTICE QIGONG"
~ Bianca

To reach Bianca Molle,
visit www.mettamorphix.com

Made in the USA
Monee, IL
07 March 2021